A Cold, Cold Day

By Pamela Chanko

ISBN: 978-1-338-88865-2

Editor: Liza Charlesworth
Art Director: Tannaz Fassihi; Designer: Tanya Chernyak
Photos ©: 6: Chubykin Arkady/Shutterstock.com; 7: gorillaimages/Shutterstock.com; 8: Yuganov Konstantin/Shutterstock.com. All other photos © Getty Images.

1 2 3 4 5 6 7 8 9 10   68   31 30 29 28 27 26 25 24 23
Printed in Jiaxing, China. First printing, January 2023.

SCHOLASTIC INC.

It is a cold, cold day!
Time to ride on a sled.

It is a cold, cold day!
Time to build a snowman.

It is a cold, cold day!
Time to throw a snowball.

It is a cold, cold day!
Time to ice skate.

It is a cold, cold day!
Time to build a fort.

It is a cold, cold day!
Time to make a snow angel.

It is a cold, cold day!
Time to get warm.